Jesus and the Children

Written by
Etta G. Wilson

Illustrations by
Gary Torrisi

Publications International, Ltd.

When Jesus began teaching and preaching, he remembered his own childhood. He knew how much his family had cared for him.

As a boy, Jesus helped Joseph in the carpenter's shop. He played with the other children in the town. He went to the synagogue to learn how the people worshiped God.

Jesus loved children very much. As he got older, he always kept a special place in his heart for them.

When Jesus grew up, he would go from town to town teaching people about God. Often, he would help children who were sick or who had other problems.

One day, when Jesus was teaching, a man named Jairus came over and knelt at Jesus' feet.

"My daughter is about to die!" said Jairus. "Please come and touch her so she will live."

Jesus nodded and went with Jairus. Many people followed.

ᕋᕐᑎ

Before they got to Jairus's home, some people came to meet them, saying, "Your daughter is dead! There's no need for Jesus to come."

But Jesus said to Jairus, "Don't be afraid. Just have faith!"

At Jairus's house, they saw a crowd crying for the dead girl. Jesus went into the house and said to everyone, "Why are you crying so much? The child isn't dead. She's just sleeping."

Jesus went to the child's room with her father and mother and three of his disciples. He took her hand and said, "Little girl, get up!"

And she did! The girl got up and started walking around. Everyone in the room was amazed. The girl's mother hugged her.

"Don't tell anyone what happened here," Jesus said.

There was much happiness in Jairus's house that day!

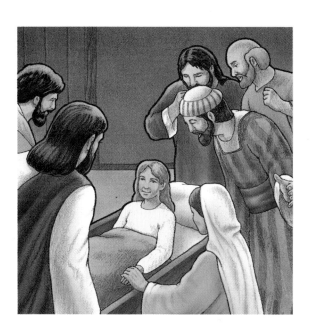

Another day, Jesus was on the road to Jerusalem. He and his disciples were tired. Jesus had been to many places and talked to many people about God's kingdom. Jesus decided to sit and rest by the side of the road for a while.

Some people saw the group relaxing by the roadside. They brought their children over to ask Jesus to bless them. But the disciples stopped them.

"Jesus is tired. Don't bother him now," they said.

But Jesus saw the children, and he told the disciples to let them pass. "Let the children come to me. Don't try to stop them."

So the disciples stood back, and the children shyly came closer to Jesus. He reached out and hugged them close in his arms. Then he blessed them.

"God's kingdom is for children and people who are like them," Jesus told the disciples. "Children have a special place in God's kingdom."

Sometimes, children were helpers for Jesus. One day, Jesus was teaching a large crowd near the Sea of Galilee. Many people had brought their children to hear Jesus.

Jesus welcomed them. He told them about God's kingdom and cured those who were sick.

At the end of the day, the crowd was hungry, but there was no food. One boy in the crowd had five small loaves of bread and two fish.

There were about five thousand people in the crowd. Jesus called the boy over and asked him if he would share his bread and fish. The boy smiled and handed his lunch to Jesus.

Jesus took the bread in his hands and gave thanks to God for it. Then the disciples began to pass out the bread and fish to the people until everyone had plenty to eat.

Then Jesus asked his disciples to gather the leftover food so that nothing would be wasted.

One day, the disciples of Jesus asked him, "Who will be greatest in the kingdom of heaven?"

Jesus called over a boy who was playing nearby and asked him to stand in front of the disciples. He said, "Unless you become like a child, you will never enter the kingdom of heaven. Anyone who welcomes a child in my name, welcomes me."

The disciples then understood how important it is to be simple like a child. They also saw how special children were to Jesus.